A Friendly Field Trip

by Natalie Behar
illustrated by Molly Delaney

Harcourt
SCHOOL PUBLISHERS

Printed in China

ISBN 10: 0-15-351041-2
ISBN 13: 978-0-15-351041-0

Ordering Options
ISBN 10: 0-15-350602-4 (Grade 5 On-Level Collection)
ISBN 13: 978-0-15-350602-4 (Grade 5 On-Level Collection)
ISBN 10: 0-15-357966-8 (package of 5)
ISBN 13: 978-0-15-357966-0 (package of 5)

4 5 6 7 8 9 10   0940   12 11 10 09

CAST

SYD

IAN

BEV

TRACEY

JULIA

RUSSELL

RICK

MS. PRICE

Act One, Scene 1

The stage is set like a classroom. Students, including IAN, TRACEY, RUSSELL, and BEV, sit in rows of desks. Their teacher, MS. PRICE, stands in front.

MS. PRICE: Before we leave, I need to give you tonight's homework. We've been chosen to have a letter exchange with another class. You will each be paired with a student from the other class. Tonight your homework is to write a letter telling this student something about yourself.

BEV: With a class from another country?

MS. PRICE: Actually, it's with a class in town—but it's a class at a different school: all of the students are sight-impaired.

RUSSELL: You mean, blind?

MS. PRICE: Well, since the students can see to different degrees, "impaired" is more accurate. However, some of the students cannot see at all, yes.

TRACEY (*Deflated*)**:** Then how are they going to be able to read our letters?

IAN: Just because they can't see well doesn't mean they can't read. There are other ways to read, you know.

MS. PRICE: Good point, Ian. All of the students are proficient in Braille, and their teacher is going to transcribe our letters into Braille for them.

RUSSELL: I've never had a pen pal before, but I've always wanted one.

MS. PRICE: I'm glad to hear that, Russell. I hope you all are excited to write these letters, and I hope you'll do your best—

The bell interrupts her. Students spring up from their desks.

Act One, Scene 2

IAN, RUSSELL, BEV, *and* TRACEY *are at baseball practice.*
RUSSELL *pitches to* BEV, *who swings an imaginary bat at
an imaginary ball. All the kids follow the "ball" with their
gaze; they twist their heads around to watch the ball as Bev
strolls around the bases. Her teammates cheer.* IAN *steps up
nervously.* TRACEY *picks up the "ball" and walks up to the
pitcher's mound.*

TRACEY: Hey, Russell—it's not fair if you monopolize
the pitcher's mound all practice. (RUSSELL *steps aside as*
TRACEY *takes a pitching stance.*) Ready?

IAN *nods nervously.* TRACEY *winds her arm up and releases.*
IAN *swings and misses.*

BEV (*Encouragingly*)**:** Come on, Ian!

TRACEY *winds up again as* SYD, *an older man, appears in the background to pick up* IAN. *None of the other students see him except* IAN. TRACEY *releases her pitch.* IAN *is startled when the ball nearly hits him, causing him to whirl in a circle.*

TRACEY: Hey, Ian! Wake up!

The other students notice SYD.

IAN: Okay, okay—I'm ready!

IAN *holds his "bat" in position.* TRACEY *winds up again.*

TRACEY: We'll see about that.

Act Two, Scene 1

IAN *and* SYD *walk home from ball practice in silence.*

SYD: Hey, neighbor, you seem awfully quiet today. Is everything okay? You still want to come over to my place to bake cookies?

IAN: Sure! I was just thinking. (*Pauses somberly*) Can I ask you something, Syd?

SYD: Sure.

IAN: As far as I can tell, you can do everything I can do—though sometimes in different ways—but people make such a big deal about . . .

SYD: . . . being blind?

IAN: Yes.

SYD: Well, it does change things. There are many things you do one way that I have to do differently.

IAN: Like reading? We can both read books. You read books in Braille, and I read books for sighted people. We can read the same book, but we do so in different ways.

SYD (*Chuckles to himself*): That's very true. I often think that people are afraid of things that are different or unfamiliar. When you first met me, you were more than a little curious. I remember one day overhearing you ask your father why I walked with a cane.

IAN: I remember that. I thought you had a problem walking.

SYD: Do you remember the first night I babysat you? You asked your mom how could I look after you when I couldn't see you.

IAN: Wow, that was rude of me.

SYD: I didn't think you were being rude. You just didn't know the answer.

IAN: Well, I certainly did know the answer after that night. I had so much fun hanging out with you. We stayed up late and listened to music. Hey, that just gave me an idea. Maybe if people actually *knew* people who were sight-impaired, they'd see that they really aren't that different! I wonder how we could do this for my class.

SYD: I'm sure that enterprising mind of yours will think of a solution.

Act Two, Scene 2

MS. PRICE *stands in front of the class.*

MS. PRICE: You've been begging me to take you on a field trip, and now we're finally going to go on one—to the new wildlife conservatory! (*Cheers from the students*) You have a fellow student to thank for this great plan—we're going to go with the class we've been exchanging letters with!

BEV: You mean with the sight-impaired students?

MS. PRICE *nods.*

MS. PRICE: We're going to a *petting* zoo at the conservatory. Please have your permission slips signed and bring them back by Friday. Otherwise, you risk missing out on a very fun trip!

Act Three

It's the day of the field trip. Various stuffed animals are placed throughout the stage to resemble a petting zoo. Pen pals from each class are paired up. The pen pals introduce themselves to each other.

MS. PRICE: Stick close to your partners! If you have any problems, talk to a chaperone. Otherwise, enjoy yourselves, and we'll meet for lunch.

Students drift apart, most enjoying themselves as they observe and pet the "animals." However, TRACEY *and her partner,* JULIA, *seem to be having trouble getting on their way.* IAN *and his partner,* RICK, *walk over to them.*

IAN: Do you two need any help?

TRACEY: *No . . .* we are both doing what we want to do.

RICK: You're supposed to be helping each other. How is your partner going to know where you are going, Tracey?

JULIA: Don't worry about us. I know where she is. (IAN *is taken aback.* TRACEY *looks at* JULIA, *impressed.*)
Tracey, let's go check out the goat.
You can smell it a mile away, no?

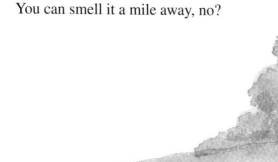

TRACEY *nods, completely enraptured as* JULIA *walks skillfully with her white cane. Without thinking,* TRACEY *steps from the grass onto the pathway, not seeing a bicyclist approaching fast behind her.* JULIA *reaches out a hand toward* TRACEY *as if about to push* TRACEY *off the pathway.*

JULIA: Tracey! Watch out for that biker! (*Reaches out to push* TRACEY *out of the way.*)

The BICYCLIST *misses* TRACEY *by a few centimeters.* TRACEY *gets her balance as* IAN, RICK, *and* MS. PRICE *come over.*

MS. PRICE: Is everyone okay?

TRACEY (*Stammers*): Uh . . . yes. Thanks to Julia. She just saved me—she kept me from getting smashed by that bicycle.

JULIA: I heard the bike coming. I'm sure you would have done the same. Let's go find the goat. It's too cumbersome to have all these people gathered around us.

TRACEY: I hear you. I'm sorry we got off to a bad start, Julia. Can we start over?

JULIA: Sure, pen pal! Now we're friends, too.

TRACEY: Would you like some assistance?

JULIA: Yes, please. Just hold out your arm to me.

TRACEY *offers her arm to* JULIA, *who takes it. The two of them chat happily as they make their way to the goats.*

Think Critically

1. Did you enjoy this play? Why or why not?

2. Compare and contrast Ian and Tracey.

3. What will probably happen the next time Tracey meets a person who is sight-impaired or who has another disability?

4. What was the author's purpose in writing this play?

5. What views of the author might be supported by this play?

 Math

Braille Look up the Braille numbers in a book or on the Internet. Write some simple math problems using Braille numbers. Exchange your math problems with those of a classmate to solve.

School-Home Connection Take the play home and read it with a family member. Then try to memorize one scene and perform it without using the book as an aid.

Word Count: 1,258

GRADE 5
Lesson 22
WORD COUNT
1,258
GENRE
Play
LEVEL
See TG or go Online

Go
online Harcourt Leveled
Readers Online Database

ISBN-13: 978-0-15-351041-0
ISBN-10: 0-15-351041-2

90000

9 780153 510410

Harcourt
SCHOOL PUBLISHERS

Whales of the World

by John Stewart

illustrated by Stephen Marchese